SING MUSICAL THEATRE

FOUNDATION (GRADES 1–3)

ANY DREAM WILL DO

AND 14 OTHER SONGS FROM THE SHOWS

INTRODUCTION

In this book we have chosen 15 songs from a wide variety of shows and movies – some very well known, others less so – all of which offer specific performing challenges suitable for foundation-level singing and musical theatre students.

The best musical theatre songs are little plays with a beginning, a middle and an end. During the course of the song a character or group of characters will explore an idea, learn something, make a decision or change in some way. It is the performer's job to convey this to the audience with clarity, conviction and understanding.

In order to do this it is essential that the performer knows where the character is, what is happening in the story at that point, who the character is singing to and why s/he is expressing those ideas at that moment. So in the **BACKGROUND** to each song we have provided some key information about plot, characters and the dramatic situation, along with a brief summary of the history of the musical from which it comes.

The **PERFORMANCE NOTES** offer some starting points for interpretation and performance. Many of the observations and acting approaches can be applied to other songs in the collection (and indeed elsewhere), so we hope that as students and their teachers explore the different songs in the book they will develop a variety of approaches to preparation and rehearsal which they can start to apply to a range of repertoire.

The **SINGING TIPS** suggest some technical exercises appropriate to the particular style or demands of each song. The intention is that over time these will help students build up a range of techniques which will help develop their singing along with their acting and movement skills.

Each introduction ends with a section entitled **BEYOND THE SONG** which reflects on one key aspect of the song and suggests topics for further discussion. Some of these relate specifically to performance, others to historical, social or environmental issues which we hope will stimulate students to relate their performance work to the wider world.

The CD contains backing tracks for each of the 15 songs. While these may be used in performance, they are intended primarily as an aid to rehearsal and preparation. Again, tempi and dynamics provide a starting point only and are not intended to be 'definitive'. Performers who have the opportunity to work with a piano accompanist should explore the musical possibilities of each score, which will enable them to further refine and nuance their performances and to make them uniquely personal, uniquely their own.

Above all we hope you enjoy singing and performing these songs – and that your audience enjoy watching you do so.

John Gardyne, Chief Examiner in Drama and Speech Subjects, Trinity College London
Luise Horrocks, Singing teacher and Associate Chief Examiner, Trinity College London

© 2011 by Faber Music Ltd and Trinity College London
First published in 2011 by Faber Music Ltd
in association with Trinity College London
Bloomsbury House
74–77 Great Russell Street
London WC1B 3DA
Music processed by SEL Engraving
Cover design by Lydia Merrills-Ashcroft
Printed in England by Caligraving Ltd
All rights reserved

ISBN10: 0-571-53555-0
EAN13: 978-0-571-53555-2

CD produced and arranged by Paul Honey
© 2011 by Faber Music Ltd and Trinity College London
℗ 2011 by Faber Music Ltd and Trinity College London

Reproducing this music in any form is illegal and forbidden by the Copyright, Designs and Patents Act, 1988.

To buy Faber Music or Trinity publications or to find out about the full range of titles available, please contact your local music retailer or Faber Music sales enquiries:

Faber Music Ltd, Burnt Mill, Elizabeth Way, Harlow, CM20 2HX England
Tel: +44(0)1279 82 89 89   Fax: +44(0)1279 82 89 90
sales@fabermusic.com   fabermusicstore.com

ANY DREAM WILL DO

JOSEPH AND THE AMAZING TECHNICOLOR® DREAMCOAT

BACKGROUND

Based on a story from the Book of Genesis, *Joseph...* tells the story of the favourite son of Jacob. Joseph's 11 brothers grow jealous of him, steal his multi-coloured coat and attempt to murder him before eventually selling him into slavery in Egypt. In prison Joseph discovers his ability to interpret dreams and rises to become the Pharaoh's right-hand man. When famine strikes, the brothers arrive in Egypt seeking help. Joseph tests his would-be murderers and eventually forgives them.

PERFORMANCE NOTES

This number comes at the end of the show, when Joseph recalls his adventures and reflects on what he has learnt. There are 3 sections to the song: a sad acknowledgement of the fact that he was originally a spoilt young man (when he was blissfully unaware that 'someone was weeping'); a dramatic middle section where he remembers how he was thrown into darkness and 'left alone'; and a wish that he might 'return to the beginning' and start again. You should aim to give each section its own dramatic quality and experiment with contrasting ways of staging them.

This is a very catchy tune, so take great care not to let the soothing, hypnotic melody and easy rhythm take over and obscure the personal, haunting lyrics. Joseph meditates on the mysterious relationship between dreams and reality, the past and the future, himself and the world he lives in. To keep these ideas fresh, try to relate some of the lyrics to your own hopes and fears for the future.

SINGING TIPS

The vocal line in this song is quite smooth and flowing, and there is quite a range from bottom to top. Make sure you can access the highest notes without pushing or squeezing the sound. Try doing the following exercises to work the higher register of your voice:

Imagine you are calling to a friend across a wide canyon. Wave and call *yoo hoo!* to attract their attention. You will instinctively pitch this high and loud, but without pushing. Try this with the word *hello* as well.

Think of a small puppy that has got lost. Make some high whining sounds that it might make to get people to notice it.

Pretend it's bonfire night and there are lots of rockets going off. Try whooping as a rocket goes up. Feel the excitement as it explodes!

BEYOND THE SONG

Writing team Tim Rice and Andrew Lloyd Webber considered writing a musical about a James Bond-type spy, but abandoned it in favour of the Joseph story. Why do you think they did that? What elements contribute to a good plot for a musical?

ANY DREAM WILL DO

MUSIC BY ANDREW LLOYD WEBBER
LYRICS BY TIM RICE

6

BE KIND TO YOUR PARENTS
FANNY

BACKGROUND

Fanny is a tale of lost love and family secrets, set in the French port of Marseilles. After her boyfriend Marius runs away to sea, Fanny discovers that she is pregnant. In desperation she marries Panisse, an elderly sail maker, who brings up her child Cesario as his own. When Cesario is 12 he breaks their hearts by running away to be with his real father. But Marius returns him to his mother and the dying Panisse, and the show ends on a note of reconciliation and forgiveness as Fanny gives her son this 'piece of good advice'.

PERFORMANCE NOTES

Although *Fanny* is largely forgotten now, 'Be kind to your parents' has survived as a popular song for children to perform. The upbeat, jaunty tune perfectly supports the mock-serious tone of the lyrics. A young performer might imagine being a bossy, short-tempered teacher addressing an inattentive class. Make sure you relish the rather pompous use of 'adult' language ('a difficult stage of life ... daily storm and strife') and emphasise the final point of your lesson (that some day the pupils will be parents too). Don't try and get a laugh on this line: the more solemn and serious you are, the funnier it will be. And of course an adult audience will always appreciate the humour of being lectured to by a small child.

When considered in the context of the show, however, the song becomes something completely different. An older, more mature performer must remember that this is a mother singing to her wayward 12-year-old son whom she nearly lost forever. You know you may have failed him in many ways, and you know that you have done many 'foolish things', but you desperately need his kindness and understanding. How much of your own emotional turmoil is it appropriate to show your child? How do the teacher-like lyrics and the nursery-rhyme simplicity of the tune help you control the complex mix of feelings you might be feeling at this moment? And how might you change the way you sing in the last line?

SINGING TIPS

This song needs lots of energy but mustn't rush. This means being very connected to the pulse of the music.

Memorise a section, and then march around the room as you sing, using big movements to help you stay in time. You could also swing your arms. Try practising singing and marching at different speeds and see how the level of energy changes. This is a good exercise to help you choose the speed you want for the song. Remember: plenty of life and energy but don't let the song run away from you! You could try saying the words as well as singing them, especially having fun with the word 'incredible'.

BEYOND THE SONG

Fanny opened on Broadway in 1954 to good reviews, ran for 888 performances and was later produced in London. But the show has only rarely been revived in recent years. What makes a show go out of fashion? Which current musical theatre hits do you think will survive?

BE KIND TO YOUR PARENTS

WORDS AND MUSIC BY HAROLD ROME

Freely

Here's a piece of good ad-vice.

Think it ov-er once or twice.

Be

Rhythmic (like a polka) ♩ = 80

kind to your par-ents, tho' they don't de-serve it. Re-

A COMMON BOY

GREAT EXPECTATIONS

BACKGROUND

Charles Dickens' *Great Expectations* tells the story of an orphaned blacksmith's apprentice boy called Philip Pirrip ('Pip'), who discovers that he has a mysterious secret benefactor. This song comes from a musical adaptation of the novel by Gerry Flanagan and Annemarie Lewis Thomas, first performed by Youth Music Theatre UK [†] in August 2007.

When he is 7 years old, Pip is summoned to the house of Miss Havisham, a wealthy and eccentric spinster, who orders him to play cards with Estella, a young girl whom she has just adopted. This is Estella's reaction.

PERFORMANCE NOTES

In Dickens' time there was a vast gulf between the rich and the poor. Pip – although by no means destitute – lives in a humble cottage with his sister. Estella lives in a vast mansion and has everything she could possibly wish for. So the two children really are 'poles apart'. In preparing Estella's song you might want to look at portraits of the Victorian period to see what wealthy young girls wore and the manner in which they presented themselves.

Estella notes her reactions to Pip one by one – his appearance, his clothes, his smell. How might she conceal her distaste for this common boy? The music is brisk, her thoughts come quickly, rushing in on one another. What does this tell you about the way her mind works and how she feels about the situation she's in?

It's important that you don't make Estella a caricature of an upper-class snob. Even though her initial reactions to Pip are quite predictable, note how she considers what his point of view might be and starts to take an interest in him by the end of the song. Do you think she is in any way changed by her encounter with Pip?

SINGING TIPS

In this song notice the repeated use of the dotted quaver–semiquaver pattern. This figure always comes on the first beat – the strongest beat – of the bar. This gives each phrase a kick of energy at the start. Make sure you keep these rhythms very crisp.

Sing up and down a fifth using the dotted rhythm: *doo-bee-doo-bee-doo-bee-doo-bee-doo*. Then try singing this with even quavers. Can you sing up to dotted rhythms and down to straight? And the other way round?

BEYOND THE SONG

'A common boy it's fairly plain to see – so working class.' What does the idea of 'class' mean to you? How – if at all – do you encounter it in your culture? Do you think the idea still has relevance in the 21st century?

[†] Youth Music Theatre UK was founded in 2003 and is now Britain's largest organisation providing participation in musical theatre projects and productions for young people. For more information about Youth Music Theatre UK, its Musical Theatre Library and how to perform this work, go to www.youthmusictheatreuk.org.

A COMMON BOY

WORDS AND MUSIC BY ANNEMARIE LEWIS THOMAS

This boy is rough, his hands be-trayed him when he dealt. This boy is rough, I should have guessed the way he smelt. He has no class, why should I play with such a boy? I guess that I could see him as my full size play-ground toy. We have the hand we're dealt yet play from diff-'rent packs.

14

FAT SAM'S GRAND SLAM
BUGSY MALONE

BACKGROUND

Bugsy Malone is a 1976 movie musical set in Prohibition-era New York and features a cast of rival gangsters, molls, small-time hoods, young hopeful chorus girls and saucy vamps. Children played all the roles, giving the film a quirky charm that is unique. The 1990s stage adaptation – also written for a cast of children – has become a favourite with youth groups and amateur theatres.

Welcome to Fat Sam's Grand Slam Speakeasy – the only place to be and be seen in New York!

PERFORMANCE NOTES

This is a great 'welcome to the nightclub' song – like 'All That Jazz' in *Chicago*. In the movie it's sung by a variety of characters – the band pianist, two female vocalists, a chorus line of dancing girls – as customers arrive for the evening. If you're working with a group, this offers wonderful opportunities for staging. Alternatively it is an excellent song for a solo singer – perhaps even Fat Sam himself.

It's important to convince your audience that this place is really interesting and fun – and that's partly because it's illegal and scandalous. Don't let it get too raunchy though: this isn't 'Hey Big Spender', it's an upbeat, goodtime song written for a cast of children.

The *da-da-da-da-da* section really cries out for a dance routine – time to show off your Twenties-style tap skills!

SINGING TIPS

Make sure you've planned exactly where you're going to breathe, and practise taking quick, silent breaths. Don't let your breathing become too shallow though. To ensure clear words, remember that your tongue mustn't be tense. Try the following:

Flap your tongue about, up and down, as quickly as you can. You can make an *er* sound as you do this.

Sing up and down a fifth on an *ar* with your tongue hanging out.

Now sing *oo* and move your finger up and down between your lips to make a loud whoop!

BEYOND THE SONG

In the movie, much of the singing was actually performed by adults, with the child cast miming along to a soundtrack. Both the director and composer have subsequently regretted this, feeling that it gives the numbers a strange, unreal quality. Years later, Paul Williams wrote: 'Perhaps I should have given the kids a chance to sing the songs.' What do you think? What does this tell us about how singing, speaking and acting relate to each other in musical theatre?

FAT SAM'S GRAND SLAM

WORDS AND MUSIC BY PAUL WILLIAMS

TRACK
4

FLASH, BANG, WALLOP!
HALF A SIXPENCE

BACKGROUND

Half a Sixpence, based on HG Wells' 1905 novel *Kipps*, tells the story of Arthur Kipps, a draper's apprentice who inherits a fortune, neglects his sweetheart, loses his fortune, gets his girl back, marries her, gets his fortune back and finds happiness at last. The musical was specially written as a showcase for the talents of Tommy Steele, one of the most popular British all-round performers of the 1960s. Throughout the show Arthur bursts into song at every available opportunity. His wedding photograph provides another one that is too good to miss.

PERFORMANCE NOTES

Although the dramatic setting for this song is clearly established ('All lined up in a wedding group, here we are for a photograph'), it quickly turns into a music-hall song: part wedding celebration, part cockney knees-up, part comic history lesson. Arthur is singing this song purely to entertain his guests, so you need to concentrate on entertaining your audience too. The song's rather 'saucy' humour is typically English, and needs cheekiness and charm to pull off successfully.

There are five verses to the song and you may not wish to perform all of them as a solo. If you are working in a group you might share the verses out. Either way, make sure you research the background to the characters that are mentioned and fully understand the meaning of all the words and phrases ('Gretna Green', 'folio', 'birthday suit').

You might try acting out some of the stories in the verses, or if you're working in a group, get other performers to do so as you sing. Even if you don't consider yourself a dancer, you should perform the claps and stamps in the refrain with commitment and energy. Enjoy yourself – it's a party!

SINGING TIPS

This song needs lots of energy! Make sure you set a speed for your performance that conveys this, but be sure not to go so fast that your audience lose the words. When you're singing at speed, there's not much time to breathe.

See how silently you can inhale. If you make lots of noise as you breathe in, this can mean that your throat is tight. When you laugh, your throat is nice and relaxed. Practise laughing! Try thinking of a good joke and enjoying the laughter. Then see if you can keep the sensation of laughing without making any sound. If you can do this while you sing the song, your quick breathing won't affect your throat. Keep those shoulders nice and loose all the time too.

BEYOND THE SONG

For many people, this song – and indeed all of *Half a Sixpence* – is inescapably associated forever with Tommy Steele's performance. What qualities do you think make a performance 'definitive'? What challenges does this present performers who subsequently play the role?

FLASH, BANG, WALLOP!

WORDS AND MUSIC BY DAVID HENEKER

1. All lined up in a wed-ding group, here we are for the pho-to-graph. We're
(2.) same thing hap-pened long a - go, when man was in his prime, and
(3.) read it in a fo - li - o, or seen the Shakes-peare play, how

all dressed up in a morn-ing suit all try-ing not to laugh. Since the
what went on we on - ly know, from the snaps he took at the time. When
Ju - li - et fell for Ro - me - o in the mer-ry month of May. When he

23

JUST ONE PERSON

SNOOPY – THE MUSICAL

BACKGROUND

Snoopy – the Musical presents the 'Peanuts' cartoon characters created by Charles M Schulz in a series of scenes and songs that explore the bittersweet world of childhood: friendship, dreams, relationships with pets and animals, first love, plans for the future, and the difficulty of finding your place in the world.

At the end of the show, Charlie Brown stares out into the night sky. His faithful dog Snoopy sings him this simple song of loyalty and self-belief, and gradually his other friends join in one by one.

PERFORMANCE NOTES

Performers working in a group: This song gathers in intensity as it moves from a solo, to a duet, to a trio, to the whole company singing together. As the lyrics are repeated by more and more performers ('deep enough and strong enough ... hard enough and long enough') they gain power and conviction, proving to Charlie Brown that nobody is truly alone so long as someone, somewhere, believes in them.

Solo performers: If there is no 'Charlie Brown' on stage, you might perform the song as someone singing to him or herself, gradually realising that there are other people – parents, family, friends – on whom they can always rely. Look at the lyrics carefully. How might you use the repeated words and phrases to convey a sense of growing self-belief and hope?

SINGING TIPS

Singing this song as a soloist means working on dynamics as the excitement and joy grow through the music. If you choose to get louder as the song progresses, you need to make sure the tone stays bright and free. To prepare, try the following exercises:

Breathe in deeply and then hiss. See if you can keep the sound very even. Can you hiss for a reasonable length of time? Keep practising until you feel comfortable.

Do the same again but this time crescendo (get louder) as you hiss. You should feel your tummy muscles working as you increase the sound.

Try singing one note on an *or* sound to a count of four, getting louder. Don't suddenly get loud – make it gradual. Remember, don't force the sound!

BEYOND THE SONG

The 'Peanuts' characters are known and loved as very simple, two-dimensional, black-and-white drawings. Snoopy has a very distinct non-human shape. Woodstock is a tiny bird. What challenges do set and costume designers face in putting this world onto the stage? How would you do it?

JUST ONE PERSON

WORDS AND MUSIC BY HAL HACKADY AND LARRY GROSSMAN

TRACK
6

LET'S GO FLY A KITE

MARY POPPINS

BACKGROUND

Walt Disney's 1964 film *Mary Poppins* is one of the best-loved movie musicals of all time. The story is set in London in 1910. Stuffy banker Mr Banks cannot control his headstrong wife or his wayward children Jane and Michael. One day the household is turned on its head by the arrival of the 'practically perfect' Mary Poppins, who becomes the children's nanny and, after a series of magical adventures, eventually teaches the family to love and respect each other. In the final scene, the Banks family join a joyous crowd flying kites in a London park, while Mary Poppins – her work done – leaves forever.

PERFORMANCE NOTES

This looks like a very simple song. In an earlier scene, Jane and Michael ask Mr Banks to mend their kite but he is preoccupied with his work and refuses. Now – having lost his job and realising what is truly important in life – he mends the kite and takes them out to fly it. But what he's really saying in the song is that he has learnt that it takes very little ('tuppence for paper and strings') to transform a person's outlook and gain a whole new understanding of the joy of life (to 'soar' high in the sky like a bird).

There's no need to try to convey this hidden meaning (sometimes known as the 'subtext') in your performance. Concentrate on the simple fun of flying a kite in a park or on a beach – or better still, go out and do it for real. Feel the tug of the string, the wind in your face, your excitement as the kite goes ever higher. Then experiment with how you can make these feelings clear for your audience. As long as you are aware of the subtext, it will usually take care of itself in performance!

SINGING TIPS

This is a very happy song. You need to communicate this, but if you smile too much when you sing, the sound can become squeezed and tense. You need to practise looking happy with your eyes while keeping your jaw nice and loose to let the sound stay free and projected. Try the following exercise:

Screw your face up with eyes tight closed and mouth scrunched up. Then open your face up completely with eyes and mouth wide open. Think surprised. Try doing this a few times in a row.

Then see if you can open your mouth wide while smiling with the eyes. Keep thinking of things that make you really happy. Look in a mirror to see if this is working and remember to smile with the eyes as you sing this song.

BEYOND THE SONG

The 2004 London stage version of *Mary Poppins* made various changes to the film, and several new songs were added. In this version, 'Let's go fly a kite' is sung at the beginning of Act 2 by Jane and Michael, Bert the chimney sweep and a park keeper. Why do you think the writers made this change? What is gained – and what is lost – by taking Mr and Mrs Banks out of the song?

LET'S GO FLY A KITE

WORDS AND MUSIC BY RICHARD M SHERMAN AND ROBERT B SHERMAN

A LOVELY LEGGY POTION

THE MERMAID

BACKGROUND

Hans Christian Andersen's 1837 fairy tale *The Little Mermaid* tells the story of a mermaid who gives up her voice and her life in the sea for the love of a human prince. It has been adapted for the stage, ballet, television and movies many times. The 1983 stage adaptation from which this song comes is more faithful to Andersen's original than many versions. It ends with Oriana the mermaid giving up her life for the love of her prince and being transformed into the foam that dances forever on the waves of the sea.

When Oriana rescues Prince Ivarr from a shipwreck, she falls in love with him at first sight. She longs to visit the human world and make her love known, but can't do so as long as she remains a mermaid. Against the advice of her family and friends, she turns to the mysterious Sea Witch, who agrees to help her in exchange for her voice. In this song the Sea Witch prepares the potion that will transform Oriana's mermaid's tail into human legs.

PERFORMANCE NOTES

The Sea Witch may be thoroughly evil, but there are many opportunities to create a richly entertaining character in the performance of the song. Even though she complains bitterly about how things have deteriorated since the 'good old days', she still goes about her work with a great deal of energy and enjoyment. Notice how much care she takes in cleaning her equipment and brewing up the potion. The song moves along rapidly and you may have to find inventive ways to act out all the detail of the scene in the time available.

There are two short dance breaks in the song. How might a witch dance? And what would this tell an audience about her mood in the scene?

SINGING TIPS

In this song you need to think about your voice communicating the character of the witch. This means experimenting with how a witch would sound, so try the following exercise:

Think of a witch laughing. You need to be able to cackle, so have some fun experimenting with cackling laughter. Try this as loud as you can (don't force your voice though!). Then try it more softly. Now see how high you can cackle and how low. Listen to how the sound changes. Think how you might work some of these sounds into your singing of this song.

BEYOND THE SONG

Though the original story ends with the mermaid dissolving into the sea, Andersen later added a final section in which 'The Daughters of Air' promise her that she will gain a human soul in 300 years – but this will only happen if children behave well. Many critics have criticised this ending and feel that Andersen changed the story in order to 'blackmail' children into being well behaved. What do you think?

A LOVELY LEGGY POTION

LYRICS BY HIAWYN ORAM
MUSIC BY CARL DAVIS

TRACK
8

MAYBE

ANNIE

BACKGROUND

Annie is a feisty 11-year-old who escapes from Miss Hannigan's orphanage and goes in search of her real parents. The show was a huge hit when it opened on Broadway in 1977 and has since been revived in thousands of productions and made into a feature film. The first scene is set in the orphanage dormitory on a winter's night in 1933. Annie's parents abandoned her there when she was a tiny baby, but left a note promising they would return for her. When 6-year-old Molly wakes from a bad dream and calls desperately for her mother, Annie comforts her by imagining her own parents, whom she hopes will come to take her home one day.

PERFORMANCE NOTES

Although the images of family life that Annie conjures up are a bit dull (pouring coffee, paying bills), it's important to remember that, for her, these tiny, everyday moments feel both hugely familiar and yet impossibly distant. When singing the opening lines you might imagine you are looking at old black-and-white photographs of people you half recognise and places you dimly remember from your dreams, so far away and yet so near. Notice how she changes the song into a kind of guessing game ('Bet'cha they're young') at bar 21. Remember that Annie is singing this song to keep up Molly's spirits – and her own.

Experiment with ways of varying your delivery in the second verse. Do the lyrics feel more or less personal? Does your mood change during the course of the song? Why might this be and how might you convey this in performance? Notice how the repeated use of the word 'maybe' throughout perfectly expresses Annie's mixture of hope and sadness on this cold winter's night. Maybe my parents will come for me. But, then again, maybe they won't. But maybe, just *maybe*, they will...

SINGING TIPS

Say the first few words of this song out loud. Can you feel how the lips come together on the *mm* sounds in 'maybe' and 'may'? Exaggerate this and you will feel the lips pinch together. Try humming on one note and then pinch the lips together. You don't want to do this when you sing, or the sound will get tight. So, practise humming with loose lips. When you sing the *mm* sounds in the words, keep your lips just as loose.

BEYOND THE SONG

Many of the best-known musicals of all time feature orphaned children who are forced to make their own way in the world. Think of Annie, Oliver, Cosette in *Les Miserables*, and Dorothy in *The Wizard of Oz*. Why do you think musical theatre is so well suited to telling their stories?

MAYBE

LYRICS BY MARTIN CHARNIN
MUSIC BY CHARLES STROUSE

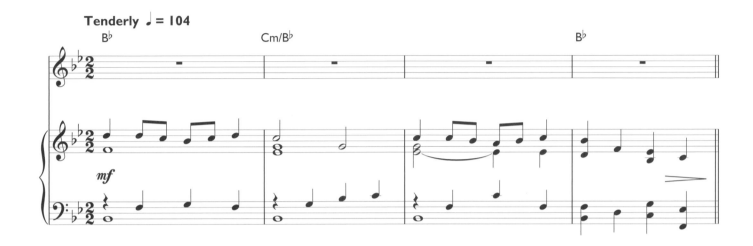

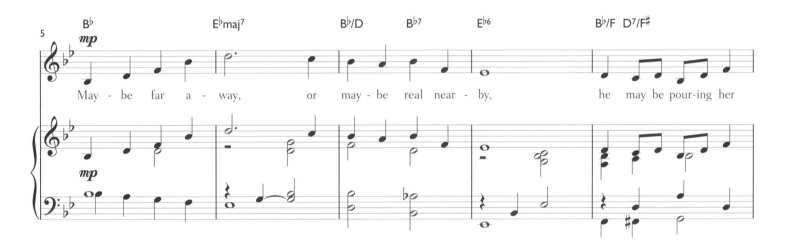

May - be far a - way, or may - be real near - by, he may be pour - ing her

cof - fee, she may be straight-'ning his tie. May - be in a house all

44

MOONSHINE LULLABY

ANNIE GET YOUR GUN

BACKGROUND

The plot of *Annie Get Your Gun* (1946) revolves around the love-hate relationship between rival fairground sharpshooters Annie Oakley and Frank Butler. The show is packed with wonderful characters, brilliant jokes and an outstanding score by Irving Berlin which never stops reminding us that 'There's no business like show business'. The role of Annie was originally played by Broadway legend Ethel Merman.

When hillbilly Annie Oakley beats Frank Butler – the star of Buffalo Bill's Wild West Show – in a shooting contest, she is immediately invited to join the company as its latest star attraction. As she and her little sisters and brothers travel on an overnight train to Minneapolis, she sings them to sleep.

PERFORMANCE NOTES

When the children first ask Annie to 'sing us a piece' she replies: 'Every time I sing you to sleep, I go to sleep and you stay awake'. That's an excellent warning for a performer. Although this is a lullaby, don't fall into the trap of being too dreamy yourself, letting your energy slip away and becoming lazy in delivery, posture and diction.

Look carefully at the words of the song. Take time to envisage the scene: the mountainous landscape, the father working at his illegal still by moonlight, his return to the house at dawn. How might you bring those images to life? If you're working with a group you might consider acting out the scene as you sing it or use it as a starting point for improvisation.

The thought that 'mamma' and 'pappy' are always watching over you as you sleep is enormously comforting for children – and for the parents too. So is the fact that the night will soon be over and the sun will rise. Make sure these important ideas are clearly expressed in your delivery.

SINGING TIPS

Look at what the composer has done to stop you becoming too dreamy in your singing. The swing rhythms could become too lazy but the strong underlying pulse will keep the energy going.

Try tapping out the rhythms on a table, saying the words out loud in rhythm and then singing sections of the song to a repeated *Kar* sound. Notice how the *k* sound gives the singing impetus. Don't make the rhythms too jerky though, or the phrasing of the song will be spoilt. Sing through parts of the song on just one vowel sound to remind yourself of the feeling of linking all the notes together.

BEYOND THE SONG

Although Ethel Merman died in 1984, her reputation as one of the great musical theatre performers lives on. She was often described as 'larger than life' both on and off stage. What does that expression mean to you? Do you think it's always a useful quality for a performer to have?

MOONSHINE LULLABY
WORDS AND MUSIC BY IRVING BERLIN

TRACK
10

Slow blues ♩ = 80

Be-hind the hill there's a bu-sy lit-tle still___ where your Pap-py's work-ing in___ the

moon - light.___ Your lov - in' Paw is - n't quite with - in the law,___ so he's

MY FAVOURITE THINGS
THE SOUND OF MUSIC

BACKGROUND

In *The Sound of Music*, novice nun Maria leaves her convent to become governess to the 7 children of stern widower Captain Von Trapp. She teaches them to sing, marries their father, and the family become successful concert performers in Austria before fleeing from the Nazis. The 1965 film version of the show became the most popular movie musical of all time.

The writers of the movie version made several changes to the original script. In the stage show, Maria and the Mother Abbess sing 'My favourite things' shortly before Maria leaves the convent to take up her post as governess. In the movie version it is sung later on in the story, when the children are frightened by a thunderstorm and come to Maria's bedroom to be comforted.

PERFORMANCE NOTES

This kind of song is sometimes referred to as a 'shopping list' song – the verses simply list a series of phrases or objects that have no real connection with each other. Because there's no strong story-telling or emotional content to songs like this, there is a danger that the audience will lose interest and stop listening or – worse! – that the performer will start mixing up the lines. So your challenge is to make the audience feel like they are hearing the song for the first time and that it has a unique personal meaning for you.

What might be in that brown paper package? A favourite present you once received? Or a gift you gave to someone else? Who is that girl in a white dress? Your sister? Your best friend? A picture of your grandmother when she was a little girl?

Once you've really got the audience's attention, use the final section to tell them why you do this – to keep your spirits up when times are bad. And so now they know how to do the same thing.

SINGING TIPS

Crisp consonants will help you project the words in this song. Say *k-b-k-b-w-m* out loud a few times, making the sounds really strong. Can you feel how your tongue and lips move differently with the different sounds?

Now sing through a few phrases, making sure your lips and tongue are working well. If you work the consonants too hard you will end up creating accents. For most of this song, accents are not needed, so take care. However, when you get to the phrases 'When the dog bites' and 'When the bee stings', you might like to add accents to make the *b* of 'bites' and the *st* of 'stings' very firm.

BEYOND THE SONG

Despite its huge success at the box office, not everyone enjoyed *The Sound of Music*. Some critics found it too sweet and sentimental, and Pauline Kael from *The New York Times* famously called it 'the sugar-coated lie people seem to want to eat'. Why do you think she called it a 'lie'?

MY FAVOURITE THINGS

LYRICS BY OSCAR HAMMERSTEIN II
MUSIC BY RICHARD RODGERS

TRACK
11

54

PART OF YOUR WORLD

THE LITTLE MERMAID

BACKGROUND

Hans Christian Andersen's evergreen fairy tale was transformed into an animated film by the Walt Disney studios in 1989. The movie changed the original story's tragic ending (see the earlier notes on *The Mermaid* on page 38) and in this version the mermaid Ariel lives happily ever after with Prince Eric.

Ariel is intrigued by humans. She has often swum to the surface and observed them, and has collected lots of human objects retrieved from sunken ships. But her father King Triton disapproves of her interest and forbids her to return. Ariel sits, surrounded by her collection, unable to understand her father's attitude: 'I don't see how a world that makes such beautiful things could be bad.'

PERFORMANCE NOTES

It's important that you set this song very clearly in Ariel's private space, where she keeps her 'trove' of treasures – almost like her bedroom. You might use some props to create this scene. Remember too that she's just had a big argument with her father.

As the song progresses, Ariel's ideas develop logically, and you may find it useful to speak the lyrics out loud to help you identify these stages. After a rather hesitant start, her language becomes more active (*I wanna be where the people are*), she acquires new vocabulary (*what d-ya call 'em, oh feet*), and she begins to envisage herself in the human world (*spend a day warm on the sand*). The song moves towards a pivotal moment in bar 64, where the word 'stand' has a double meaning (to stand on human legs and to stand up to her father), which leads to a wonderfully confident and assured final verse.

SINGING TIPS

In this song there is a real sense of Ariel thinking out loud. This means you'll need to think about how to give your performance enough space to communicate your thoughts to the audience.

Try experimenting with slowing down the speed at certain points to achieve this. For example, Ariel asks herself questions such as *what d-ya call 'em…* and *what's that word again …* Take time to pause a little so that you can think the answer before you sing it.

At the end there is a change of mood. Think what this change is and then see if changing the speed and altering how loudly you sing can help to communicate this. Don't be in a hurry to finish this song!

BEYOND THE SONG

When the film was first released, some critics felt that the happy ending spoilt the message of Andersen's story. In their original versions, several famous fairy tales, like *Little Red Riding Hood* and *Cinderella*, are quite violent and have tragic outcomes which some adults now think are entirely unsuitable for children. What do you think?

PART OF YOUR WORLD

WORDS BY HOWARD ASHMAN
MUSIC BY ALAN MENKEN

TRACK
12

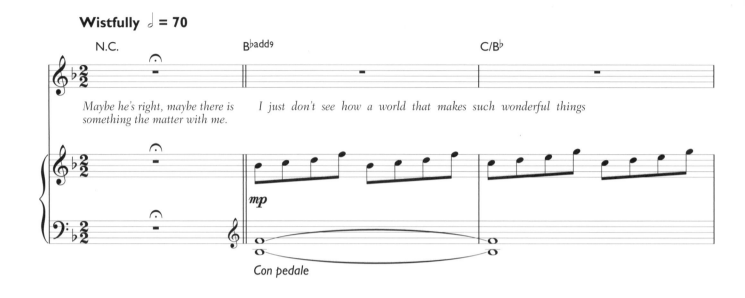

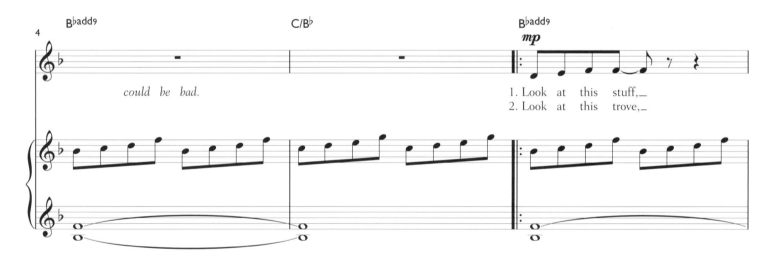

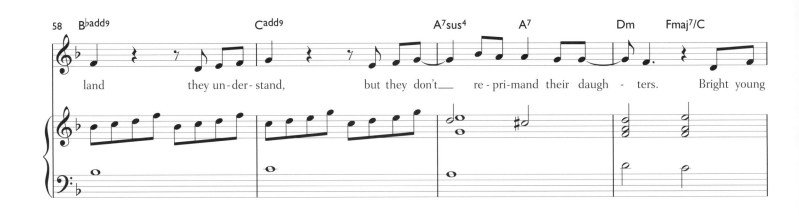

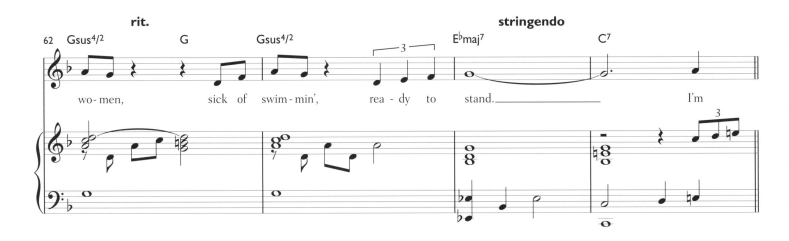

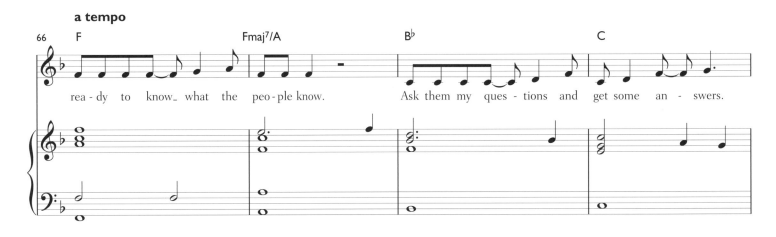

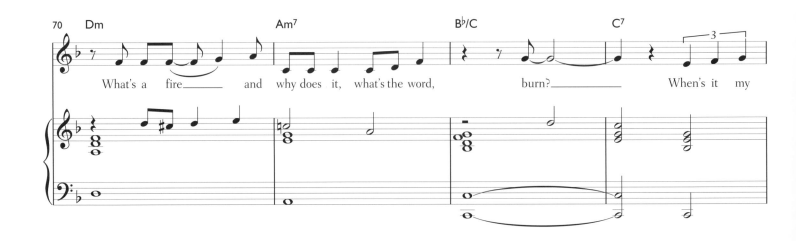

ROUND-SHOULDERED MAN

THE SECRET GARDEN

BACKGROUND

Frances Hodgson Burnett's classic children's novel *The Secret Garden* was published in 1911 and has since been adapted many times for movies, television and stage. This song comes from the 1991 version.

When her parents die in a cholera epidemic in India, 11-year-old Mary Lennox is sent to live with her uncle Archibald – a moody, introverted hunchback – in gloomy Misselthwaite Manor in Yorkshire. One night Mary follows the sound of someone crying to an upper bedroom and meets Colin, Archibald's son, a bedridden invalid. His mother dead years before, desperately lonely and neglected by his father, Colin describes his dreams to Mary.

PERFORMANCE NOTES

This song contributes to a delicate, sensitive scene set late at night in a big spooky house. Colin never sees anybody apart from the servants and never leaves his room, so it is a new experience for him to have another child of his own age to talk to. It's unlikely that he's ever told anyone about his dreams before, so he may have to dig deep into his memory to recall the details. How might you convey this to an audience?

Read the lyrics of the song carefully. What do they tell you about Colin's feelings about his father, his illness and the world outside his bedroom? Notice that he repeats the last two lines of the song at the end. Why do you think he does this?

SINGING TIPS

This song has some long phrases and also some long held notes. When practising, make sure you count the beats in your head as you sing. Think carefully of the sense of the words and where you can best breathe without upsetting the meaning. To help with your breathing, try this exercise:

Imagine you are chewing bubble gum. Have a good chew and really enjoy it. Now stop chewing and put your hand next to your mouth. Pretend you're pulling out a string of the gum. Keep pulling slowly as your arm stretches out.

Now try doing this while you're singing one of the long phrases of the song. Keep your hand moving all the time and don't reach the end of your stretch until the end of the phrase. You may need to try this a few times so that you can match your hand movement exactly to the speed and length of the phrase.

BEYOND THE SONG

The novelist Robert Louis Stevenson described dreams occurring in 'that small theatre of the brain which we keep brightly lighted all night long'. Some people write down their dreams every morning when they wake up. What do you think our dreams tell us about ourselves?

ROUND-SHOULDERED MAN

WORDS BY MARSHA NORMAN
MUSIC BY LUCY SIMON

66

THE WASPISH TANGO

THE BEES KNEES

BACKGROUND

Originally commissioned by the City of London School for Girls, *The Bees Knees* was first performed in June 2005 by a cast of 120 children between the ages of 7 and 11.[†]

The Bees Knees is set in and around a beehive. When a young bee named Phoebe objects to the bees electing a king rather than a queen, she is banished from the hive and forced to seek her fortune in the outside world. One dark night she wanders in to the territory of a gang of wasps. They threaten and bully her, but when she stands up to them they are impressed by her bravery and offer their help. In this song Daz, the leader of the gang, explains to Phoebe how wasps see the world.

PERFORMANCE NOTES

At the beginning of the song, Daz – who can be played by a boy or a girl – tells Phoebe about the tough life a wasp has in early childhood. What tone of voice might be appropriate for this? How might your mood change once the main tune and rhythm start at bar 19?

In the original production the wasps played on kazoos and danced from bar 64 onwards. What aspects of their character might you aim to express through the dance? The tango originated in South America. It has many forms and styles, but typically tango dancers hold their bodies in an upright posture and move in very strict rhythms. You can create your own version of the wasps' dance. But make sure you have enough breath left to sing the last phrases of the song.

SINGING TIPS

This song is all about rhythm and feeling the movement of the dance in the music. Triplets are a big feature of this movement and you need to make sure you can sing them very evenly.

Although the tango here is for wasps, for this exercise you need to think of a bumble bee! Try saying *bumble bee* out loud. Notice that there are 3 syllables: see how evenly you can say them. Now try singing *bumble bee* on one note and then repeat it a few times. Can you keep the pitch and stay in time? Have some fun moving up and down scales with *bumble bee* and then see if you can think of other words that fit triplets. As we are thinking of insects, how about *ladybird* or *centipede?*

BEYOND THE SONG

Bees, wasps and other insects play a vital role in maintaining the delicate equilibrium of the natural world, but modern farming methods and destruction of their habitats now threaten the survival of many species. In the UK in the last few years, 3 out of 25 native species of bumble bee have become extinct – and the situation in other countries is far worse.

[†] All enquiries regarding performance rights for *The Bees Knees* should be sent to drama@trinitycollege.co.uk.

THE WASPISH TANGO

WORDS BY JOHN GARDYNE AND MATTHEW MILLER
MUSIC BY MATTHEW MILLER

TRACK 14

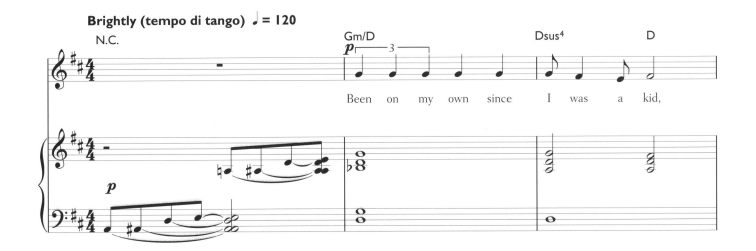

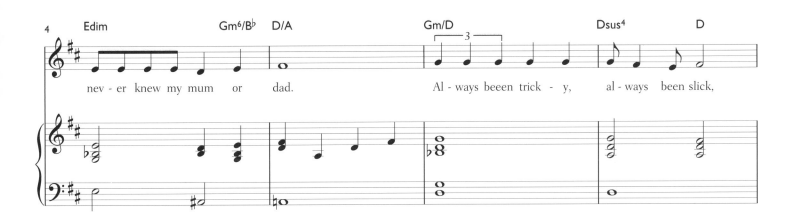

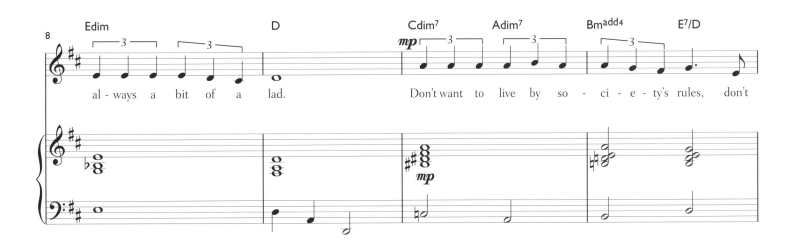

72

WHERE IS LOVE?
OLIVER!

BACKGROUND

Lionel Bart's musical adaptation of Charles Dickens' 1838 novel *Oliver Twist* was an immediate hit when it was first performed in London in 1963, subsequently transferring to Broadway for a record-breaking run and being made into an Oscar-winning movie. With its classic storyline, tuneful music hall-influenced score and cast of colourful London characters, it remains one of the very few truly British musicals to have established itself as a firm favourite with audiences all over the world.

Oliver Twist is an orphan boy living in a grim London workhouse in Victorian London. One day he asks for a second helping of gruel and is branded as a troublemaker and thrown out. He is sold to an undertaker for 3 guineas (a little more than £3), who makes him sleep in the cellar under his shop where the coffins are stored. Alone in the dark, Oliver sings about the mother he never knew.

PERFORMANCE NOTES

The first time we meet Oliver he is in the workhouse, which is overcrowded, noisy and run by cruel adults who terrorise the young boys in their care. In preparing for this song, try to imagine the day he's just had: he's been publicly humiliated, hauled round the streets of London, and sold to someone he has never met. And yet this may be the first real moment of peace, quiet and solitude that he has ever experienced.

Don't fall into the trap of just 'being sad' as you perform this song. Notice how every line in the song is a question — questions to which Oliver desperately wants to know the answers. He is not wallowing in self pity — he is actively trying to work out his feelings about his mother and the world he finds himself in — and thinking about what he must do to get out of this situation and find happiness. In performance, how might you convey to the audience that these are new ideas that Oliver is exploring for the first time?

SINGING TIPS

There are lots of rising scale passages in this song, and sometimes the tuning might slip as you move higher. This exercise will help you connect to your 'thinking' voice, where you hear notes in your head.

In a comfortable range for your voice, sing up a scale to numbers from 1 to 8. Do this a few times and then choose a number to leave out. Sing up the scale again but when you get to your chosen number, leave a gap. Make sure the pitch of the following number is still accurate, so that you carry on up the scale in tune. When you can do this, try leaving out two numbers.

BEYOND THE SONG

Although *Oliver Twist* is nearly 200 years old, it is an appalling and terrible fact that slavery still exists today. The Tronie Foundation (www.troniefoundation.org) estimates that even today 27 million people in the developing world — half of them children — live in slavery and endure living and working conditions scarcely better than those of the early 19th century.

WHERE IS LOVE?

WORDS AND MUSIC BY LIONEL BART

VOCAL WARM-UPS

SOME SUGGESTIONS

Good singing in any style requires good physical control. Just like an athlete preparing for a run, a warm-up for the body and the voice before you start singing is essential.

- Start with a wake up and shake up! Tension in the wrong place is not good for singers so some movement to loosen up is a good place to start. Try the following:

  Wriggle the ankles, legs, wrists and arms.

  Lift and lower the shoulders then move the head gently from side to side. Swing the arms and try different swimming strokes – front crawl, back crawl and breast stroke.

  Jog on the spot.

- When you feel suitably loose, find your singing position. You should stand upright but not stretched with the head nice and central and the weight held evenly between the feet. Don't tense the knees or lift the shoulders.

- Now you are ready to have some fun vocalising! Sing the word 'sing' on a low note and hold the *ng* sound. Now, on the *ng* sound sing up and down like the siren on a police car. Gradually extend the range of the notes so that you 'siren' through your entire range. Keep the sound gentle but try not to let it crack. Then do the same on a *zz* sound like a bee buzzing. Then make sounds like an excited monkey, from the bottom of your voice to the top.

- The voice should now be getting ready to sing, so you just need to make sure that you are able to breathe from the right place, and with control. Put your fingers under your waist band or belt and cough gently. Can you feel the muscles move? These muscles need to work when you breathe. As you breathe in your tummy will get bigger and as you breathe out your tummy will get smaller. Think of a balloon getting bigger as it fills with air.

There is plenty more to discover about breathing and lots of different exercises you can use to warm up, but these vocal notes will get you started.